COMPACT DISC PAGE AND BAND INFORMATION

Music Minus One

Classic Themes
Student Edition Clarinet
Student Edition Trumpet

The Yankee Doodle Boy

Tempo di Marcia

George M. Cohan

Waves Of The Danube

Waltz

1 2/3 piano intro
precedes solo.

Tempo di Valse

J. Ivanovici

D. C. al Fine

3837
3245

Loch Lomond

Andante

Old Scotch Song

Dark Eyes

Gypsy Song

Allegretto

Moderato

espressivo

piu mosso

3837
3245

Gold And Silver

Waltz

1 2/3 piano intro
precedes solo.

Franz Lehar

3837
3245

Andantino

Edwin Lemare

Barcarolle
from Tales of Hoffman

2 bar piano intro
precedes solo.

Jacques Offenbach

Allegretto

3837
3245

Beautiful Dreamer

Stephen Foster

2 bar piano intro
precedes solo.

Andantino

3837
3245

Blue Danube

Waltz

2 bar piano intro
precedes solo.

Tempo di Valse

Johann Strauss

3837
3245

Ciribiribin

Allegretto

A. Pestalozza

Come Back To Sorrento

Andantino

Ernesto Di Curtis

3837
3245

Melody in F

2 bar piano intro
precedes solo.

Anton Rubenstein

Moderato

None But The Lonely Heart

Andante non tanto

Peter I. Tschaikowsky

3837
3245

The Star Spangled Banner

Con spirito

Francis Scott Key

Apache Dance

3 ½ bar piano intro
precedes solo.

Valse moderato

Jacques Offenbach

3837
3245

Tales From The Vienna Woods

Waltz

Tempo di Valse

Johann Strauss

A Media Luz

4 3/8 bar piano intro
precedes solo.

Eduardo Donato

Tango

3837
3245

Ave Maria

Andante

Franz Schubert

Country Gardens

4 bar piano solo
precedes solo.

Allegro moderato

English Folk Song

3837
3245

Evening Star

from Tannhausser

Richard Wagner

Andante mosso

Fifth Nocturne

J. Leybach

3837
3245

Humoreske

2 bar piano intro
precedes solo.

Poco lento e grazioso

Anton Dvorak

Slavonic Dance

2 bar piano intro
precedes solo.

Allegretto grazioso

Anton Dvorak

Tango

Andantino grazioso

Isaac Albeniz

3837
3245

Two Guitars

2 bar piano intro
precedes solo.

Andante con moto

Gypsy Melody

3837
3245

Moment Musical

Franz Schubert

3837
3245

Largo

from Xerxes

George F. Handel

Largo

MMO Compact Disc Catalog

BROADWAY

___	LES MISERABLES/PHANTOM OF THE OPERA	MMO CD 1016
___	HITS OF ANDREW LLOYD WEBBER	MMO CD 1054
___	GUYS AND DOLLS	MMO CD 1067
___	WEST SIDE STORY 2 CD Set	MMO CD 1100
___	CABARET 2 CD Set	MMO CD 1110
___	BROADWAY HEROES AND HEROINES	MMO CD 1121
___	CAMELOT	MMO CD 1173
___	BEST OF ANDREW LLOYD WEBBER	MMO CD 1130
___	THE SOUND OF BROADWAY	MMO CD 1133
___	BROADWAY MELODIES	MMO CD 1134
___	BARBRA'S BROADWAY	MMO CD 1144
___	JEKYLL & HYDE	MMO CD 1151
___	SHOWBOAT	MMO CD 1160
___	MY FAIR LADY 2 CD Set	MMO CD 1174
___	OKLAHOMA	MMO CD 1175
___	THE SOUND OF MUSIC 2 CD Set	MMO CD 1176
___	SOUTH PACIFIC	MMO CD 1177
___	THE KING AND I	MMO CD 1178
___	FIDDLER ON THE ROOF 2 CD Set	MMO CD 1179
___	CAROUSEL	MMO CD 1180
___	PORGY AND BESS	MMO CD 1181
___	THE MUSIC MAN	MMO CD 1183
___	ANNIE GET YOUR GUN 2 CD Set	MMO CD 1186
___	HELLO DOLLY! 2 CD Set	MMO CD 1187
___	OLIVER 2 CD Set	MMO CD 1189
___	SUNSET BOULEVARD	MMO CD 1193
___	GREASE	MMO CD 1196
___	SMOKEY JOE'S CAFE	MMO CD 1197
___	MISS SAIGON	MMO CD 1226

CLARINET

___	MOZART CONCERTO, IN A, K.622	MMO CD 3201
___	WEBER CONCERTO NO. 1 in Fm. STAMITZ CONC. No. 3 IN Bb	MMO CD 3202
___	SPOHR CONCERTO NO. 1 in C MINOR OP. 26	MMO CD 3203
___	WEBER CONCERTO OP. 26, BEETHOVEN TRIO OP. 11	MMO CD 3204
___	FIRST CHAIR CLARINET SOLOS	MMO CD 3205
___	THE ART OF THE SOLO CLARINET:	MMO CD 3206
___	MOZART QUINTET IN A, K.581	MMO CD 3207
___	BRAHMS SONATAS OP. 120 NO. 1 & 2	MMO CD 3208
___	WEBER GRAND DUO CONCERTANT WAGNER ADAGIO	MMO CD 3209
___	SCHUMANN FANTASY OP. 73, 3 ROMANCES OP. 94	MMO CD 3210
___	EASY CLARINET SOLOS Volume 1 - STUDENT LEVEL	MMO CD 3211
___	EASY CLARINET SOLOS Volume 2 - STUDENT LEVEL	MMO CD 3212
___	EASY JAZZ DUETS - STUDENT LEVEL	MMO CD 3213
___	VISIONS The Clarinet Artistry of Ron Odrich	MMO CD 3214
___	IN A LEAGUE OF HIS OWN Popular Songs played by Ron Odrich and You	MMO CD 3215
___	SINATRA SET TO MUSIC Kern, Weill, Gershwin, Howard and You	MMO CD 3216
___	STRAVINSKY: L'HISTOIRE DU SOLDAT	MMO CD 3217
___	BEGINNING CONTEST SOLOS - Jerome Bunke, Clinician	MMO CD 3221
___	BEGINNING CONTEST SOLOS - Harold Wright	MMO CD 3222
___	INTERMEDIATE CONTEST SOLOS - Stanley Drucker	MMO CD 3223
___	INTERMEDIATE CONTEST SOLOS - Jerome Bunke, Clinician	MMO CD 3224
___	ADVANCED CONTEST SOLOS - Stanley Drucker	MMO CD 3225
___	ADVANCED CONTEST SOLOS - Harold Wright	MMO CD 3226
___	INTERMEDIATE CONTEST SOLOS - Stanley Drucker	MMO CD 3227
___	ADVANCED CONTEST SOLOS - Stanley Drucker	MMO CD 3228
___	ADVANCED CONTEST SOLOS - Harold Wright	MMO CD 3229
___	BRAHMS Clarinet Quintet in Bm, Op. 115	MMO CD 3230
___	TEACHER'S PARTNER Basic Clarinet Studies	MMO CD 3231
___	JEWELS FOR WOODWIND QUINTET	MMO CD 3232
___	WOODWIND QUINTETS minus CLARINET	MMO CD 3233
___	FROM DIXIE to SWING	MMO CD 3234
___	THE VIRTUOSO CLARINETIST Baermann Method, Op. 63 4 CD Set	MMO CD 3240
___	ART OF THE CLARINET Baermann Method, Op. 64 4 CD Set	MMO CD 3241
___	POPULAR CONCERT FAVORITES WITH ORCHESTRA	MMO CD 3242
___	BAND-AIDS CONCERT BAND FAVORITES WITH ORCHESTRA	MMO CD 3243
___	WORLD FAVORITES Student Editions, 41 Easy Selections (1st-2nd year)	MMO CD 3244
___	CLASSIC THEMES Student Editions, 27 Easy Songs (2nd-3rd year)	MMO CD 3245

PIANO

___	BEETHOVEN CONCERTO NO. 1 IN C	MMO CD 3001
___	BEETHOVEN CONCERTO NO. 2 IN Bb	MMO CD 3002
___	BEETHOVEN CONCERTO NO. 3 IN C MINOR	MMO CD 3003
___	BEETHOVEN CONCERTO NO. 4 IN G	MMO CD 3004
___	BEETHOVEN CONCERTO NO. 5 IN Eb (2 CD SET)	MMO CD 3005

___	GRIEG CONCERTO IN A MINOR OP.16	MMO CD 3006
___	RACHMANINOFF CONCERTO NO. 2 IN C MINOR	MMO CD 3007
___	SCHUMANN CONCERTO IN A MINOR	MMO CD 3008
___	BRAHMS CONCERTO NO. 1 IN D MINOR (2 CD SET)	MMO CD 3009
___	CHOPIN CONCERTO NO. 1 IN E MINOR OP. 11	MMO CD 3010
___	MENDELSSOHN CONCERTO NO. 1 IN G MINOR	MMO CD 3011
___	MOZART CONCERTO NO. 9 IN Eb K.271	MMO CD 3012
___	MOZART CONCERTO NO. 12 IN A K.414	MMO CD 3013
___	MOZART CONCERTO NO. 20 IN D MINOR K.466	MMO CD 3014
___	MOZART CONCERTO NO. 23 IN A K.488	MMO CD 3015
___	MOZART CONCERTO NO. 24 IN C MINOR K.491	MMO CD 3016
___	MOZART CONCERTO NO. 26 IN D K.537, CORONATION	MMO CD 3017
___	MOZART CONCERTO NO. 17 IN G K.453	MMO CD 3018
___	LISZT CONCERTO NO. 1 IN Eb, WEBER OP. 79	MMO CD 3019
___	LISZT CONCERTO NO. 2 IN A, HUNGARIAN FANTASIA	MMO CD 3020
___	J.S. BACH CONCERTO IN F MINOR, J.C. BACH CON. IN Eb	MMO CD 3021
___	J.S. BACH CONCERTO IN D MINOR	MMO CD 3022
___	HAYDN CONCERTO IN D	MMO CD 3023
___	HEART OF THE PIANO CONCERTO	MMO CD 3024
___	THEMES FROM GREAT PIANO CONCERTI	MMO CD 3025
___	TSCHAIKOVSKY CONCERTO NO. 1 IN Bb MINOR	MMO CD 3026
___	ART OF POPULAR PIANO PLAYING, Vol. 1 STUDENT LEVEL	MMO CD 3033
___	ART OF POPULAR PIANO PLAYING, Vol. 2 STUDENT LEVEL 2 CD Set	MMO CD 3034
___	'POP' PIANO FOR STARTERS STUDENT LEVEL	MMO CD 3035
___	DVORAK TRIO IN A MAJOR, OP. 90 "Dumky Trio"	MMO CD 3037
___	DVORAK QUINTET IN A MAJOR, OP. 81	MMO CD 3038
___	MENDELSSOHN TRIO IN D MAJOR, OP. 49	MMO CD 3039
___	MENDELSSOHN TRIO IN C MINOR, OP. 66	MMO CD 3040
___	BLUES FUSION FOR PIANO	MMO CD 3049
___	CLAUDE BOLLING SONATA FOR FLUTE AND JAZZ PIANO TRIO	MMO CD 3050
___	TWENTY DIXIELAND CLASSICS	MMO CD 3051
___	TWENTY RHYTHM BACKGROUNDS TO STANDARDS	MMO CD 3052
___	FROM DIXIE to SWING	MMO CD 3053
___	J.S. BACH BRANDENBURG CONCERTO NO. 5 IN D MAJOR	MMO CD 3054
___	BACH Cm CONC. - 2 PIANOS / SCHUMANN & VAR., OP. 46 - 2 PIANOS	MMO CD 3055
___	J.C. BACH Bm CONC./HAYDN C CONCERT./HANDEL CONC. GROSSO-D	MMO CD 3056
___	J.S. BACH TRIPLE CONCERTO IN A MINOR	MMO CD 3057
___	FRANCK SYM. VAR. / MENDELSSOHN: CAPRICCO BRILLANT	MMO CD 3058
___	C.P.E. BACH CONCERTO IN A MINOR	MMO CD 3059
___	STRETCHIN' OUT-'Comping' with a Jazz Rhythm Section	MMO CD 3060
___	RAVEL: PIANO TRIO	MMO CD 3061
___	THE JIM ODRICH EXPERIENCE Pop Piano Played Easy	MMO CD 3062
___	POPULAR PIANO MADE EASY Arranged by Jim Odrich	MMO CD 3063
___	SCHUMANN: Piano Trio in D Minor, Opus 63	MMO CD 3064
___	BEETHOVEN: Trio No. 8 & Trio No. 11, "Kakadu" Variations	MMO CD 3065
___	SCHUBERT: Piano Trio in Bb Major, Opus 99 (2 CD Set)	MMO CD 3066
___	SCHUBERT: Piano Trio in Eb Major, Opus 100 (2 CD Set)	MMO CD 3067
___	POPULAR SONGS Arranged by Jim Odrich	MMO CD 3069

PIANO - FOUR HANDS

___	RACHMANINOFF Six Scenes	4-5th year	MMO CD 3027
___	ARENSKY 6 Pieces, STRAVINSKY 3 Easy Dances	2-3rd year	MMO CD 3028
___	FAURE: The Dolly Suite		MMO CD 3029
___	DEBUSSY: Four Pieces		MMO CD 3030
___	SCHUMANN Pictures from the East	4-5th year	MMO CD 3031
___	BEETHOVEN Three Marches	4-5th year	MMO CD 3032
___	MOZART COMPLETE MUSIC FOR PIANO FOUR HANDS 2 CD Set		MMO CD 3036
___	MAYKAPAR First Steps, OP. 29	1-2nd year	MMO CD 3041
___	TSCHAIKOVSKY: 50 Russian Folk Songs		MMO CD 3042
___	BIZET: 12 Children's Games		MMO CD 3043
___	GRETCHANINOFF: ON THE GREEN MEADOW		MMO CD 3044
___	POZZOLI: SMILES OF CHILDHOOD		MMO CD 3045
___	DIABELLI: PLEASURES OF YOUTH		MMO CD 3046
___	SCHUBERT: FANTASIA & GRAND SONATA		MMO CD 3047

VIOLIN

___	BRUCH CONCERTO NO. 1 IN G MINOR OP.26	MMO CD 3100
___	MENDELSSOHN CONCERTO IN E MINOR	MMO CD 3101
___	TSCHAIKOVSKY CONCERTO IN D OP. 35	MMO CD 3102
___	BACH DOUBLE CONCERTO IN D MINOR	MMO CD 3103
___	BACH CONCERTO IN A MINOR, CONCERTO IN E	MMO CD 3104
___	BACH BRANDENBURG CONCERTO NOS. 4 & 5	MMO CD 3105
___	BACH BRANDENBURG CONCERTO NO. 2, TRIPLE CONCERTO	MMO CD 3106
___	BACH CONCERTO IN DM, (FROM CONCERTO FOR HARPSICHORD)	MMO CD 3107
___	BRAHMS CONCERTO IN D OP. 77	MMO CD 3108
___	CHAUSSON POEME, SCHUBERT RONDO	MMO CD 3109
___	LALO SYMPHONIE ESPAGNOLE	MMO CD 3110
___	MOZART CONCERTO IN D K.218, VIVALDI CON. AM OP.3 NO.6	MMO CD 3111
___	MOZART CONCERTO IN A K.219	MMO CD 3112
___	WIENIAWSKI CON. IN D. SARASATE ZIGEUNERWEISEN	MMO CD 3113
___	VIOTTI CONCERTO NO. 22 IN A MINOR	MMO CD 3114
___	BEETHOVEN 2 ROMANCES, SONATA NO. 5 IN F "SPRING SONATA"	MMO CD 3115

30

MMO Compact Disc Catalog

MMO Compact Disc Catalog

____ THE ART OF THE SOLO TRUMPET with Orchestral Accompaniment ....MMO CD 3807
____ BAROQUE BRASS AND BEYOND Brass Quintets ....MMO CD 3808
____ THE COMPLETE ARBAN DUETS all of the classic studies............................MMO CD 3809
____ SOUSA MARCHES PLUS BEETHOVEN, BERLIOZ, STRAUSS ....MMO CD 3810
____ BEGINNING CONTEST SOLOS Gerard Schwarz ....MMO CD 3811
____ BEGINNING CONTEST SOLOS Armando Ghitalla ....MMO CD 3812
____ INTERMEDIATE CONTEST SOLOS Robert Nagel, Soloist ....MMO CD 3813
____ INTERMEDIATE CONTEST SOLOS Gerard Schwarz ....MMO CD 3814
____ ADVANCED CONTEST SOLOS Robert Nagel, Soloist ....MMO CD 3815
____ CONTEST SOLOS Armando Ghitalla ....MMO CD 3816
____ INTERMEDIATE CONTEST SOLOS Gerard Schwarz ....MMO CD 3817
____ ADVANCED CONTEST SOLOS Robert Nagel, Soloist ....MMO CD 3818
____ ADVANCED CONTEST SOLOS Armando Ghilalla ....MMO CD 3819
____ BEGINNING CONTEST SOLOS Raymond Crisara ....MMO CD 3820
____ BEGINNING CONTEST SOLOS Raymond Crisara ....MMO CD 3821
____ INTERMEDIATE CONTEST SOLOS Raymond Crisara ....MMO CD 3822
____ TEACHER'S PARTNER Basic Trumpet Studies 1st year ....MMO CD 3823
____ TWENTY DIXIELAND CLASSICS ....MMO CD 3824
____ TWENTY RHYTHM BACKGROUNDS TO STANDARDS ....MMO CD 3825
____ FROM DIXIE TO SWING ....MMO CD 3826
____ TRUMPET PIECES BRASS QUINTETS ....MMO CD 3827
____ MODERN BRASS QUINTETS..MMO CD 3828
____ WHEN JAZZ WAS YOUNG The Bob Wilber All Stars ....MMO CD 3829
____ CONCERT BAND FAVORITES WITH ORCHESTRA ....MMO CD 3831
____ BAND-AIDS CONCERT BAND FAVORITES WITH ORCHESTRA ....MMO CD 3832
____ BRASS TRAX The Trumpet Artistry Of David O'Neill ....MMO CD 3833
____ TRUMPET TRIUMPHANT The Further Adventures Of David O'Neill ....MMO CD 3834
____ WORLD FAVORITES Student Editions, 41 Easy Selections (1st-2nd year)......MMO CD 3836
____ CLASSIC THEMES Student Editions, 27 Easy Songs (2nd-3rd year) ....MMO CD 3837
____ STRAVINSKY: L'HISTOIRE DU SOLDAT ....MMO CD 3835
____ 12 CLASSIC JAZZ STANDARDS Bb/Eb/Bass Clef ....MMO CD 7010
____ 12 MORE CLASSIC JAZZ STANDARDS Bb/Eb/Bass Clef..........................MMO CD 7011

TROMBONE

____ TROMBONE SOLOS Student Level Volume 1 ....MMO CD 3901
____ TROMBONE SOLOS Student Level Volume 2 ....MMO CD 3902
____ EASY JAZZ DUETS Student Level ....MMO CD 3903
____ BAROQUE BRASS & BEYOND Brass Quintets ....MMO CD 3904
____ MUSIC FOR BRASS ENSEMBLE Brass Quintets ....MMO CD 3905
____ UNSUNG HERO George Roberts ....MMO CD 3906
____ BIG BAND BALLADS George Roberts ....MMO CD 3907
____ STRAVINSKY: L'HISTOIRE DU SOLDAT ....MMO CD 3908
____ BEGINNING CONTEST SOLOS Per Brevig ....MMO CD 3911
____ BEGINNING CONTEST SOLOS Jay Friedman..MMO CD 3912
____ INTERMEDIATE CONTEST SOLOS Keith Brown, Professor, Indiana U. ......MMO CD 3913
____ INTERMEDIATE CONTEST SOLOS Jay Friedman ....MMO CD 3914
____ ADVANCED CONTEST SOLOS Keith Brown, Professor, Indiana University ..MMO CD 3915
____ ADVANCED CONTEST SOLOS Per Brevig ....MMO CD 3916
____ ADVANCED CONTEST SOLOS Keith Brown, Professor, Indiana University ..MMO CD 3917
____ ADVANCED CONTEST SOLOS Jay Friedman ....MMO CD 3918
____ ADVANCED CONTEST SOLOS Per Brevig ....MMO CD 3919
____ TEACHER'S PARTNER Basic Trombone Studies 1st year ....MMO CD 3920
____ TWENTY DIXIELAND CLASSICS ....MMO CD 3924
____ TWENTY RHYTHM BACKGROUNDS TO STANDARDS ....MMO CD 3925
____ FROM DIXIE TO SWING ....MMO CD 3926
____ STICKS & BONES BRASS QUINTETS ....MMO CD 3927
____ FOR TROMBONES ONLY MORE BRASS QUINTETS ....MMO CD 3928
____ POPULAR CONCERT FAVORITES The Stuttgart Festival Band ....MMO CD 3929
____ BAND-AIDS CONCERT BAND FAVORITES WITH ORCHESTRA ....MMO CD 3930
____ WORLD FAVORITES Student Editions, 41 Easy Selections (1st-2nd year)......MMO CD 3931
____ CLASSIC THEMES Student Editions, 27 Easy Songs (2nd-3rd year) ....MMO CD 3932
____ 12 CLASSIC JAZZ STANDARDS Bb/Eb/Bass Clef....................................MMO CD 7010
____ 12 MORE CLASSIC JAZZ STANDARDS Bb/Eb/Bass Clef..........................MMO CD 7011

TENOR SAXOPHONE

____ TENOR SAXOPHONE SOLOS Student Edition Volume 1 ....MMO CD 4201
____ TENOR SAXOPHONE SOLOS Student Edition Volume 2 ....MMO CD 4202
____ EASY JAZZ DUETS FOR TENOR SAXOPHONE..MMO CD 4203
____ FOR SAXES ONLY Arranged by Bob Wilber..MMO CD 4204
____ BLUES FUSION FOR SAXOPHONE ....MMO CD 4205
____ JOBIM BRAZILIAN BOSSA NOVAS with STRINGS ....MMO CD 4206
____ TWENTY DIXIE CLASSICS ....MMO CD 4207
____ TWENTY RHYTHM BACKGROUNDS TO STANDARDS ....MMO CD 4208
____ PLAY LEAD IN A SAX SECTION ....MMO CD 4209
____ DAYS OF WINE & ROSES Sax Section Minus You ....MMO CD 4210
____ FRENCH & AMERICAN SAXOPHONE QUARTETS ....MMO CD 4211
____ CONCERT BAND FAVORITES WITH ORCHESTRA ....MMO CD 4212
____ BAND AIDS CONCERT BAND FAVORITES..MMO CD 4213

____ JAZZ JAM FOR TENOR (2 CD Set) ....MMO CD 4214
____ 12 CLASSIC JAZZ STANDARDS Bb/Eb/Bass Clef ....MMO CD 7010
____ 12 MORE CLASSIC JAZZ STANDARDS Bb/Eb/Bass Clef..........................MMO CD 7011

CELLO

____ DVORAK Concerto in B Minor Op. 104 (2 CD Set) ....MMO CD 3701
____ C.P.E. BACH Concerto in A Minor ....MMO CD 3702
____ BOCCHERINI Concerto in Bb, BRUCH Kol Nidrei ....MMO CD 3703
____ TEN PIECES FOR CELLO ....MMO CD 3704
____ SCHUMANN Concerto in Am & Other Selections ....MMO CD 3705
____ CLAUDE BOLLING Suite For Cello & Jazz Piano Trio ....MMO CD 3706
____ RAVEL: PIANO TRIO MINUS CELLO ....MMO CD 3707
____ RAGTIME STRING QUARTETS ....MMO CD 3708
____ SCHUMANN: Piano Trio in D Minor, Opus 63 ....MMO CD 3709
____ BEETHOVEN: Piano Trio For Cello ....MMO CD 3710
____ SCHUBERT: Piano Trio in Bb Major, Opus 99 Minus Cello (2 CD Set) ....MMO CD 3711
____ SCHUBERT: Piano Trio in Eb Major, Opus 100 Minus Cello (2 CD Set) ....MMO CD 3712
____ BEETHOVEN: STRING QUARTET in A minor, Opus 132 (2 CD Set) ....MMO CD 3713
____ DVORAK QUINTET in A Major, Opus 81 Minus Cello................................MMO CD 3714

OBOE

____ ALBINONI Concerti in Bb, Op. 7 No. 3, No. 6, D. Op. 9 No. 2 in Dm ....MMO CD 3400
____ TELEMANN Conc. in Fm; HANDEL Conc. in Bb; VIVALDI Conc.in Dm ....MMO CD 3401
____ MOZART Quartet in F K.370, STAMITZ Quartet in F Op. 8 No. 3 ....MMO CD 3402
____ BACH Brandenburg Concerto No. 2, Telemann Con. in Am ....MMO CD 3403
____ CLASSIC SOLOS FOR OBOE Delia Montenegro, Soloist ....MMO CD 3404
____ MASTERPIECES FOR WOODWIND QUINTET ....MMO CD 3405
____ THE JOY OF WOODWIND QUINTETS..MMO CD 3406
____ PEPUSCH SONATAS IN C/TELEMANN SONATA IN Cm ....MMO CD 3407
____ QUANTZ TRIO SONATA IN Cm/BACH GIGUE/ABEL SONATAS IN F ....MMO CD 3408

ALTO SAXOPHONE

____ ALTO SAXOPHONE SOLOS Student Edition Volume 1................................MMO CD 4101
____ ALTO SAXOPHONE SOLOS Student Edition Volume 2.................................MMO CD 4102
____ EASY JAZZ DUETS FOR ALTO SAXOPHONE ....MMO CD 4103
____ FOR SAXES ONLY Arranged Bob Wilber ....MMO CD 4104
____ JOBIM BRAZILIAN BOSSA NOVAS with STRINGS ....MMO CD 4106
____ UNSUNG HEROES FOR ALTO SAXOPHONE..MMO CD 4107
____ BEGINNING CONTEST SOLOS Paul Brodie, Canadian Soloist ....MMO CD 4111
____ BEGINNING CONTEST SOLOS Vincent Abato ....MMO CD 4112
____ INTERMEDIATE CONTEST SOLOS Paul Brodie, Canadian Soloist ....MMO CD 4113
____ INTERMEDIATE CONTEST SOLOS Vincent Abato ....MMO CD 4114
____ ADVANCED CONTEST SOLOS Paul Brodie. Canadian Soloist...................MMO CD 4115
____ ADVANCED CONTEST SOLOS Vincent Abato ....MMO CD 4116
____ ADVANCED CONTEST SOLOS Paul Brodie, Canadian Soloist ....MMO CD 4117
____ Basic Studies for Alto Sax TEACHER'S PARTNER 1st year level ....MMO CD 4119
____ ADVANCED CONTEST SOLOS Vincent Abato ....MMO CD 4118
____ PLAY LEAD IN A SAX SECTION ....MMO CD 4120
____ DAYS OF WINE & ROSES/SENSUAL SAX ....MMO CD 4121
____ TWENTY DIXIELAND CLASSICS ....MMO CD 4124
____ TWENTY RHYTHM BACKGROUNDS TO STANDARDS ....MMO CD 4125
____ CONCERT BAND FAVORITES WITH ORCHESTRA ....MMO CD 4126
____ BAND AIDS CONCERT BAND FAVORITES ....MMO CD 4127
____ MUSIC FOR SAXOPHONE QUARTET ....MMO CD 4128
____ WORLD FAVORITES Student Editions, 41 Easy Selections (1st-2nd year)......MMO CD 4129
____ CLASSIC THEMES Student Editions, 27 Easy Songs (2nd-3rd year) ....MMO CD 4130
____ 12 CLASSIC JAZZ STANDARDS Bb/Eb/Bass Clef ....MMO CD 7010
____ 12 MORE CLASSIC JAZZ STANDARDS Bb/Eb/Bass Clef..........................MMO CD 7011

SOPRANO SAXOPHONE

____ FRENCH & AMERICAN SAXOPHONE QUARTETS ....MMO CD 4801
____ 12 CLASSIC JAZZ STANDARDS Bb/Eb/Bass Clef ....MMO CD 7010
____ 12 MORE CLASSIC JAZZ STANDARDS Bb/Eb/Bass Clef..........................MMO CD 7011

BARITONE SAXOPHONE

____ MUSIC FOR SAXOPHONE QUARTET ....MMO CD 4901
____ 12 CLASSIC JAZZ STANDARDS Bb/Eb/Bass Clef....................................MMO CD 7010
____ 12 MORE CLASSIC JAZZ STANDARDS Bb/Eb/Bass Clef..........................MMO CD 7011

MMO Music Group • 50 Executive Boulevard, Elmsford, New York 10523, 1-(800) 669-7464
Website: www. minusone.com • E-mail: mmomus@aol.com